Friends

Going on a School Trip

By Diane Church
Photographs by
Chris Fairclough

W
FRANKLIN WATTS
NEW YORK • LONDON • SYDNEY

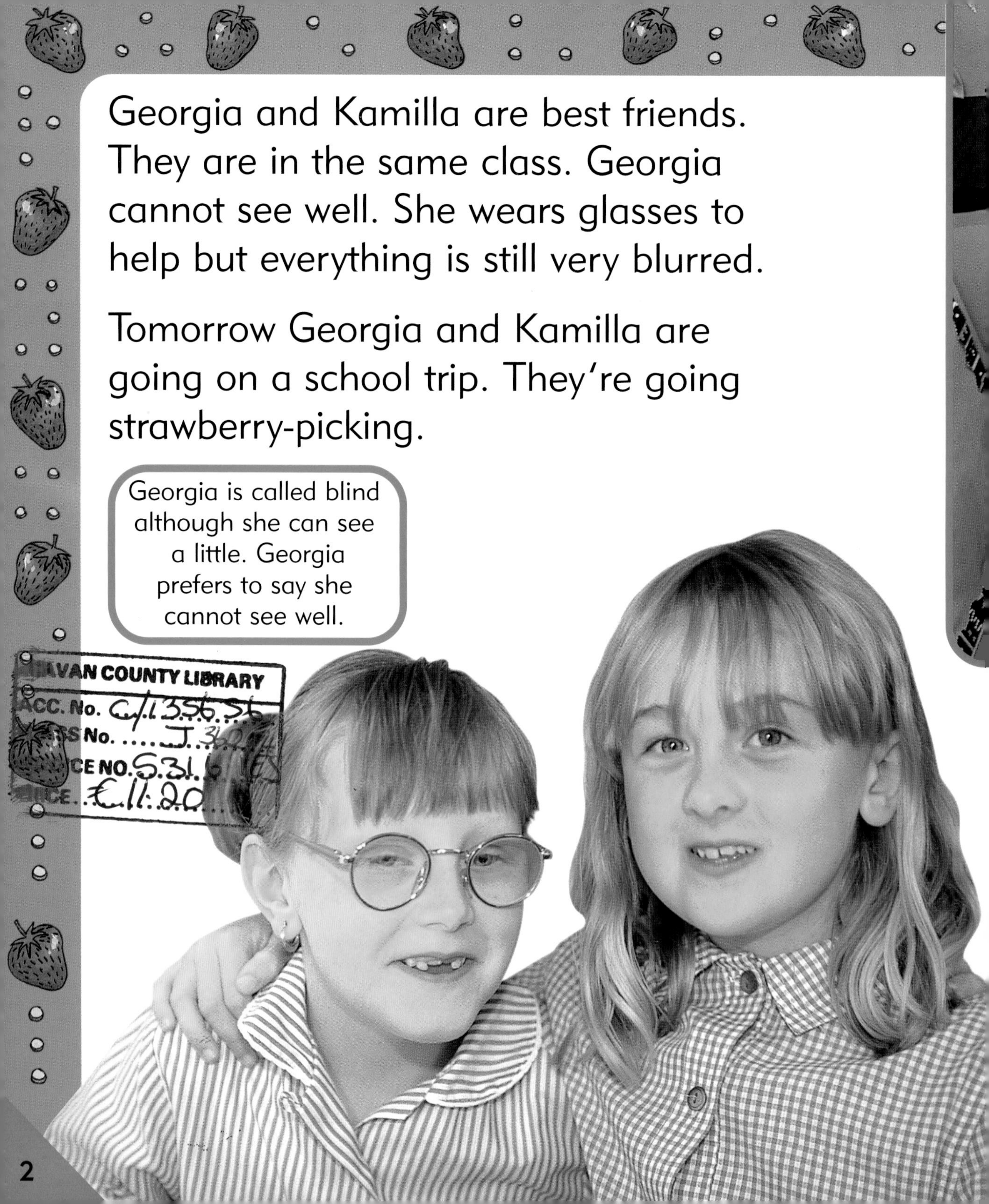

Georgia and Kamilla are best friends. They are in the same class. Georgia cannot see well. She wears glasses to help but everything is still very blurred.

Tomorrow Georgia and Kamilla are going on a school trip. They're going strawberry-picking.

Georgia is called blind although she can see a little. Georgia prefers to say she cannot see well.

"Before we go, let's read about strawberries," says their teacher, Mrs Fulton. They look at a book.

"Strawberries grow on bushes," Kamilla tells her. "And they're best when you share them!" says Georgia.

At school Georgia uses a machine to make everything look bigger so that she can see things more clearly.

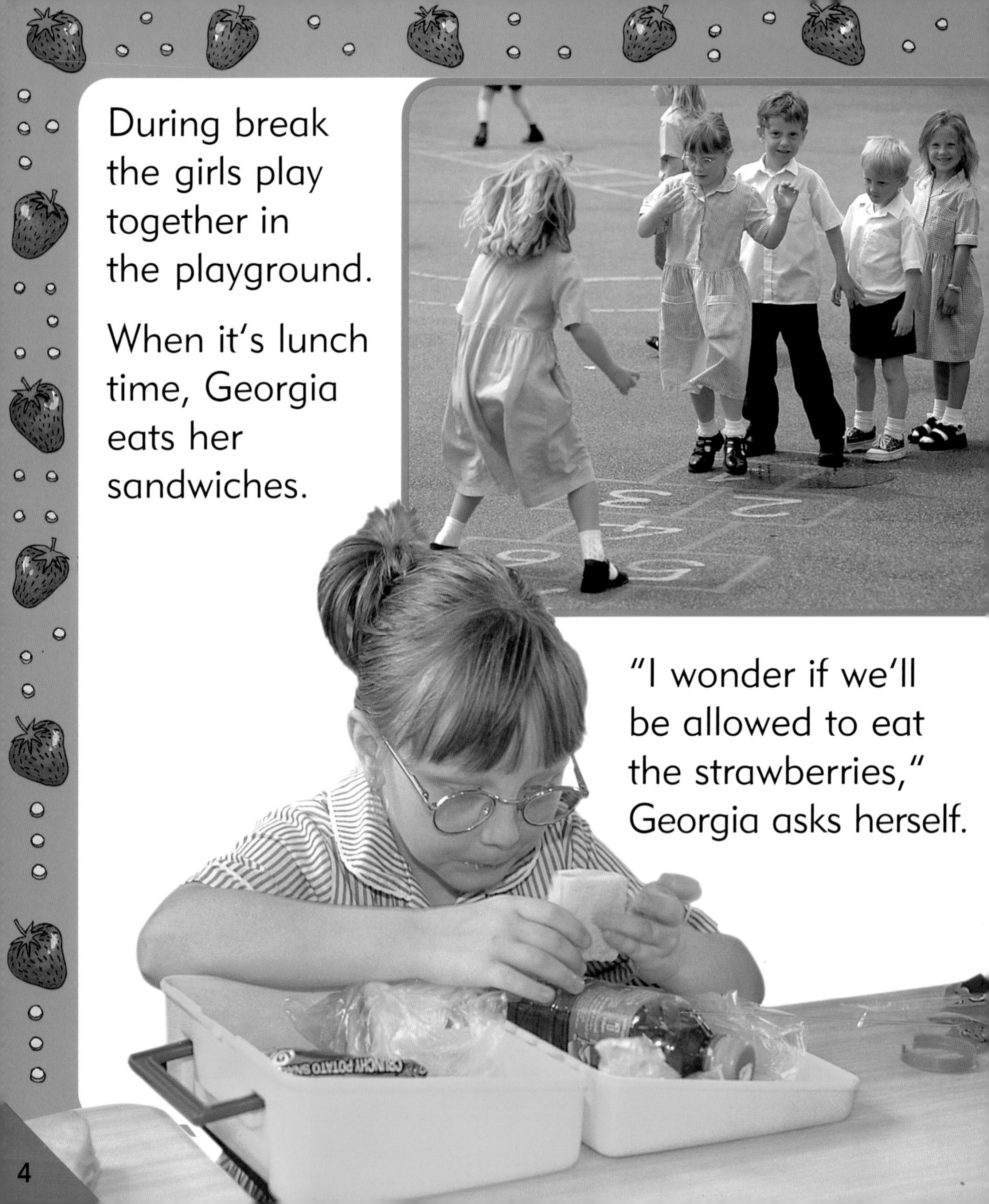

During break the girls play together in the playground.

When it's lunch time, Georgia eats her sandwiches.

"I wonder if we'll be allowed to eat the strawberries," Georgia asks herself.

After lunch, Georgia and Kamilla work on a project. "How do you spell 'tasty'?" asks Kamilla. Georgia helps Kamilla with her spelling.

Georgia uses a bright light to help her see. It helps to have her desk at an angle, too.

Then the class uses a braille display to talk about spelling. Braille is a way of writing with lots of tiny bumps.

Some people who cannot see use braille to read. They feel the bumps with their fingertips.

After school Georgia goes to stay the night at Kamilla's house. The two girls are excited about the school trip. "Do you think we'll pick a lot of strawberries?" Kamilla asks, as she helps Georgia to unwrap her chocolate cake.

Later they play with Kamilla's hamster. Georgia holds him close to her face to get a better look. "He's very fluffy and tickles!" she says, stroking his fur.

Georgia can feel the hamster moving in her hands. Touch is important for people who cannot see well.

At bedtime Georgia and Kamilla have fun looking at Kamilla's favourite books. "Some of my books are on tape so I can listen to them," Georgia tells her friend.

Georgia gets very tired as she has to look at everything so carefully. Listening to tapes is a good way for her to enjoy stories.

The next day, Kamilla tells her mum and sister about the trip on their way to school. Kamilla's mum finds a safe place to cross the road.

Georgia can tell it's safe by feeling bumps on the pavement under her feet. When it's safe to cross, she can hear the bleeps of the crossing too.

Georgia gets into the minibus and Mrs Fulton helps fit her seatbelt. "That's it!" she says. Then they set off for the strawberry farm.

At school everyone is getting ready. "How are you feeling today, Georgia?" asks one of the teachers. "Excited!" Georgia shouts.

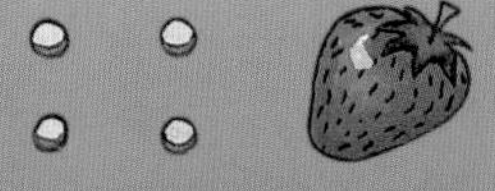

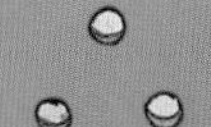

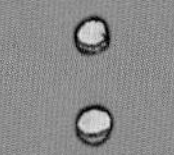
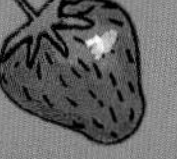
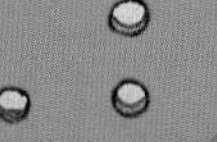

When they arrive
the farmer gives the
children a basket each.
"It's for your strawberries,"
he explains.

"Pick the bright red strawberries," says Mrs Fulton. "Like this one," she says.

Then Mrs Fulton offers her arm to help Georgia across the field. "Thank you very much," says Georgia.

"Let's see if we can find some ripe ones here," Mrs Fulton says. "Georgia, there are rows and rows of strawberry bushes stretching into the distance!" Kamilla tells her friend.

Georgia can see things very close up. Kamilla helps by telling Georgia what the field looks like.

"This is great fun!"
Georgia thinks.

Everyone is busy picking as many strawberries as they can.

Georgia finds it hard to see the strawberries. She feels and smells each one to help her find out if it's ripe.

"Have you eaten one yet?" Georgia asks Kamilla.

"Yes! They're yummy!" Kamilla says.

When everyone has picked enough fruit, the farmer weighs their boxes.
"You've picked two boxes of strawberries," the farmer tells Georgia.
"That must be a lot!" Georgia laughs.

Georgia looks closely to try to read the numbers on the scales.

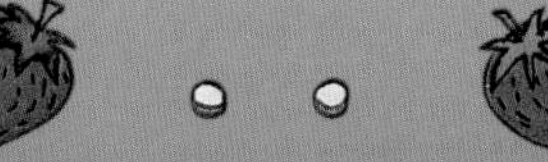

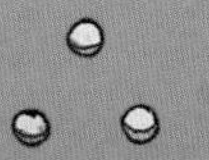

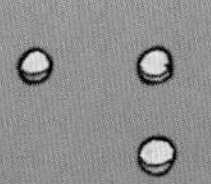
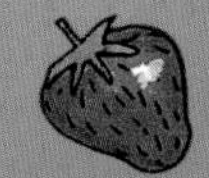
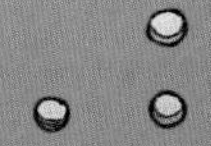

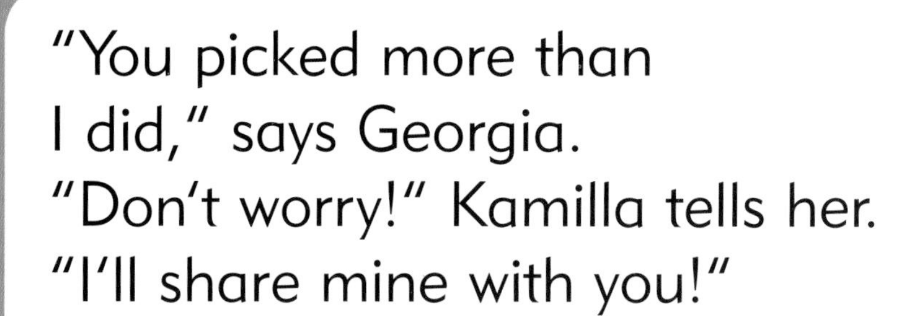

"You picked more than
I did," says Georgia.
"Don't worry!" Kamilla tells her.
"I'll share mine with you!"

"I've never seen so many
strawberries!" cries Mrs Fulton
as the children hold up their baskets.
"Can we come again soon?" Georgia and
Kamilla say. "It's been a wonderful day!"

Facts about people who are blind

Most people who are blind can see a little. They can't see very well, though. Only one blind person in twenty sees nothing at all. Most blind people can tell the difference between light and dark.

▶ This is what Georgia sees:

Everything is blurred. Imagine being in a thick fog. It is easier to see bright colours and things that are close to you, isn't it?

◀ Some blind people see this:

This person is very sensitive to light. The brightness makes colours and outlines disappear.

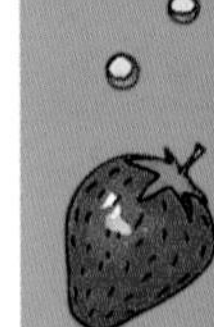

▸ Some people see this:

This person can only see a tiny part of the whole picture. It is a bit like looking through a key-hole. This is called tunnel vision.

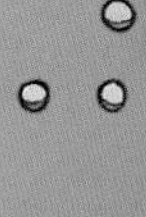

◂ Some people see this:

This person can see things clearly, but there are big blobs in front of their eyes that never go away.

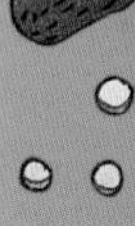

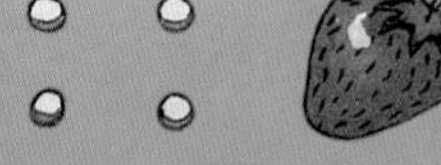

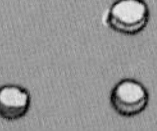

This is the alphabet in braille

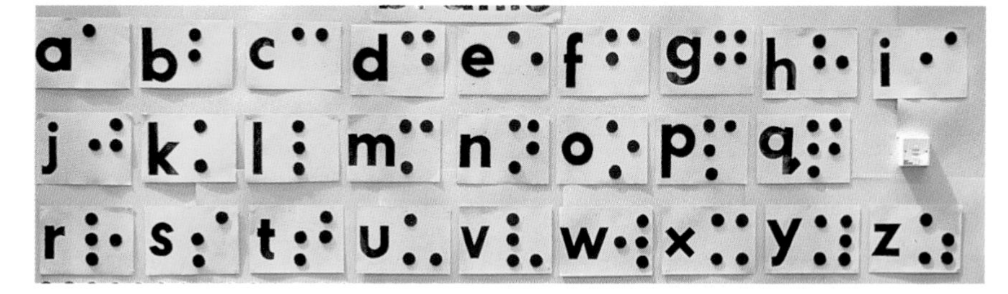

This person is reading braille.

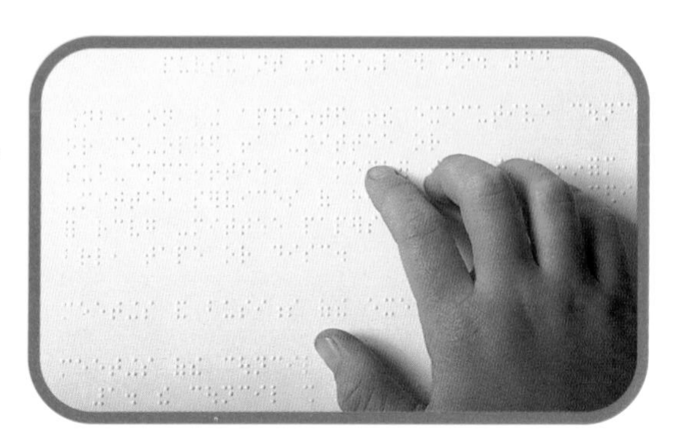

Glossary

blind when someone sees very little or nothing at all.

braille a way of writing and reading for blind people. It is made up of raised dots on a page and is read by touching the dots with the fingertips.

bumps there are bumps on the pavement to tell blind people where it is best to cross the road. Other things that blind people can use to help them get around are long white sticks or guide dogs.

Try to be helpful

★ **1.** If a blind person asks you to guide them, offer them your arm, then walk slightly in front. Never take their arm without asking first.

★ **2.** If you think a blind person needs help, ask them. People who are blind or cannot see well can manage a lot of things very well on their own.

★ **3.** Be tidy. People who cannot see well find it hard to spot things lying on the floor. They also find rubbish in the streets difficult to see.

★ **4.** Say who you are when you first speak to a blind person. It can be difficult to recognise someone from the sound of their voice.

Further information and addresses

Royal National Institute for the Blind
PO Box 173, Peterborough
PE2 6WS
http://www.rnib.org.uk.

Royal Institute for Deaf and
Blind Children,
361-5 North Rocks Road
North Rocks, NSW 2151
Sydney, Australia

REACH National Advice
Centre for Children with
Reading Difficulties
California Country Park
Nine Mile Ride,
Finchampstead, RG40 4HT
www.reach-reading.demon.co.uk

Index

Franklin Watts
96 Leonard Street
London
EC2A 4XD

Franklin Watts Australia
14 Mars Road
Lane Cove
NSW 2066

ISBN: 0 7496 3670 X

Dewey Decimal Classification Number: 362.4

10 9 8 7 6 5 4 3 2 1

A CIP catalogue record for this book is available from the British Library.

Printed in Malaysia

Consultants: Bernard Fleming (RNIB); Beverley Matthias (REACH)
Editor: Samantha Armstrong
Designer: Louise Snowdon
Photographer: Chris Fairclough
Illustrator: Eliz Hüseyin

With thanks to: Georgia Collins and her family, Kamilla Charles and her family, Linda Fulton and all the staff at Belmont Primary School, Erith; Richard Pratt, Advisory Teacher for Visual Impairment in Bexley and the Royal National Institute for the Blind.